THE ROMAN EMPIRE

Over 2000 years ago, the city and people of Rome were at the centre of the Roman Empire.

The building of this ancient empire began in Italy, in c. 753 BC. At that time, much of Europe was inhabited by tribes. To conquer a tribe, Roman armies would fight until the tribe's chief surrendered or died in battle. Some tribes rebelled and one emperor, Hadrian, even built a wall across England to stop rebel tribes invading from the north.

For years the well-trained Roman army invaded and conquered many countries. Eventually, the Roman Empire controlled part of Britain, most of Europe, North Africa and the Middle East!

ENORMOUS EMPIRE!

Colour the white areas to discover how big the Roman Empire really was!

SOLDIERING ON

At the height of the Roman Empire, a Roman soldier could travel as far away as Britannia (England), Gallia (France), Hispania (Spain) and Aegyptus (Egypt).

Where is Hadrian's wall?
AROUND HADRIAN'S GARDEN!

INVASION!

Once a tribe or territory had been conquered, the Romans began making it part of the Roman Empire. They built new towns, with new houses built of stone instead of wood. The Romans also renamed towns and countries with Roman names. Sometimes finding your way around was very confusing!

TOWN TWISTER

Can you work out what these Roman cities are known as today?

LUTETIA	WIESBADEN, GERMANY
AQUAE MATTIACAE	GENEVA, SWITZERLAND
LONDINIUM	ROME, ITALY
ROMA	PARIS, FRANCE
VINDOBONA	VIENNA, AUSTRIA
GENAVA	LONDON, ENGLAND

ROAD TO NOWHERE

The Romans connected their new towns by building long, straight roads that cut through the land. Why do you think these roads were straight?

A) THE ROMANS WERE SCARED OF CORNERS

B) THE ROMANS DIDN'T KNOW THEIR LEFT FROM THEIR RIGHT

C) THEY WANTED TO TRAVEL AS FAST AS POSSIBLE

Why did Romans build straight roads?
SO THE SOLDIERS DIDN'T GO ROUND THE BEND!

ROMAN EMPERORS

The Roman Empire was ruled by an emperor. He was a man who ruled over everyone. Augustus is thought to be the first Roman emperor, ruling from c. 27 BC to c. AD 14 for over 40 years!

ROMAN RULERS

After c. AD 68, Roman emperors were called Caesar in honour of Julius Caesar, Emperor Augustus's great-uncle.

Can you put these emperors in order of how long they reigned, writing 1 as the longest and 8 as the shortest?

10 years

2 years

22 years

13 years

42 years

21 years

7 months

21 days

Answer: 1. Theodosius II: 42 years, 2. Tiberius: 22 years, 3. Hadrian: 21 years, 4. Claudius I: 13 years, 5. Vespasian: 10 years, 6. Titus: 2 years, 7. Vitellius: 7 months, 8. Gordian I: 21 days!

MURDER! MURDER!

So how could you become Emperor? Well, usually you had to inherit the throne. That meant waiting for a relative to die, or murdering them!

IT WASN'T JUST MURDEROUS RELATIVES WE HAD TO LOOK OUT FOR. SOME EMPERORS, LIKE ME, WERE GOOD AND BROUGHT PEACE TO ROME. BUT SOME EMPERORS WERE NO GOOD AT ALL AND THEY HAD TO WATCH THEIR BACKS ALL THE TIME. LOOK AT EMPEROR CALIGULA!

Emperor Caligula

THE PRAETORIAN GUARDS WERE MY PERSONAL BODYGUARDS UNTIL THEY MURDERED ME IN AD 41, AND MADE MY UNCLE EMPEROR INSTEAD. IT DIDN'T STOP THERE EITHER. THE GUARDS PROBABLY KILLED SEVEN ROMAN EMPERORS IN TOTAL, INCLUDING ME!

Which Roman Emperor had a bad cold? JULIUS SNEEZER!

FOUL FACT!

WHAT DO EMPERORS GALBA, CLAUDIUS I, VITELLIUS, GETA, DOMITIAN, CARACALLA AND COMMODUS HAVE IN COMMON? THEY WERE ALL MURDERED!

GETA WAS MURDERED BY CARACALLA, HIS BROTHER!

EMPEROR IMPOSTOR!

Which name below is a fake emperor name?

BALBINUS   MAXIMUS EDWARDIUS   ARCADIUS

SEVERUS ALEXANDER   PETRONIUS MAXIMUS

Answer: Maximus Edwardius is the fake name!

RICH AND POOR

If you were a Roman citizen, then your life was good. If you were a wealthy Roman, then your life was better. If you were poor, it might not have been so great!

Can you spot the differences between these rich and poor Roman homes?

ROMAN LIFE

Ancient Roman life was a bit like life today. Romans brushed their teeth with toothpaste, visited the dentist and doctor, took baths and used toilets.

Sound familiar? Well, there are some

BIG
differences...

SHOPPING LIST!

Draw lines below to connect the items we use today with their Ancient Roman alternatives!

PLASTERS

TOOTHPASTE

TOILET PAPER

SOAP

A SPONGE ON A STICK

OLIVE OIL

SPIDERWEBS

POWDERED MOUSE BRAINS

Answers: Plasters for wounds – spiderwebs, toothpaste – powdered mouse brains, toilet paper – a sponge on a stick, soap – olive oil.

FOUL FACT!

THE ROMANS WENT TO THE TOILET TOGETHER! ROMAN TOILETS WERE PUBLIC. THE SEATS WERE SIDE BY SIDE AND ROMANS SHARED SPONGES, WHICH WERE USED INSTEAD OF TOILET PAPER. SOMETIMES THERE COULD BE UP TO 30 PEOPLE USING ONE TOILET AT THE SAME TIME. YUCK!

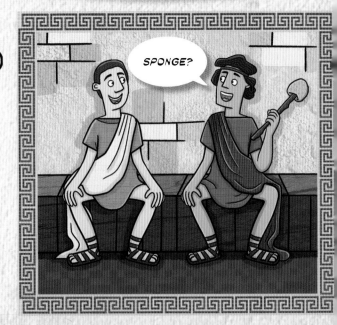

SPONGE?

CENTURION

1. Press out all the pieces.
2. Slot the stands into the base of the centurion and dress him for battle!

A 'scutum' was a shield.

stand

gladius

Crest made of horsehair or feathers.

helmet

stand

'Phalerae' were circular badges awarded for bravery.

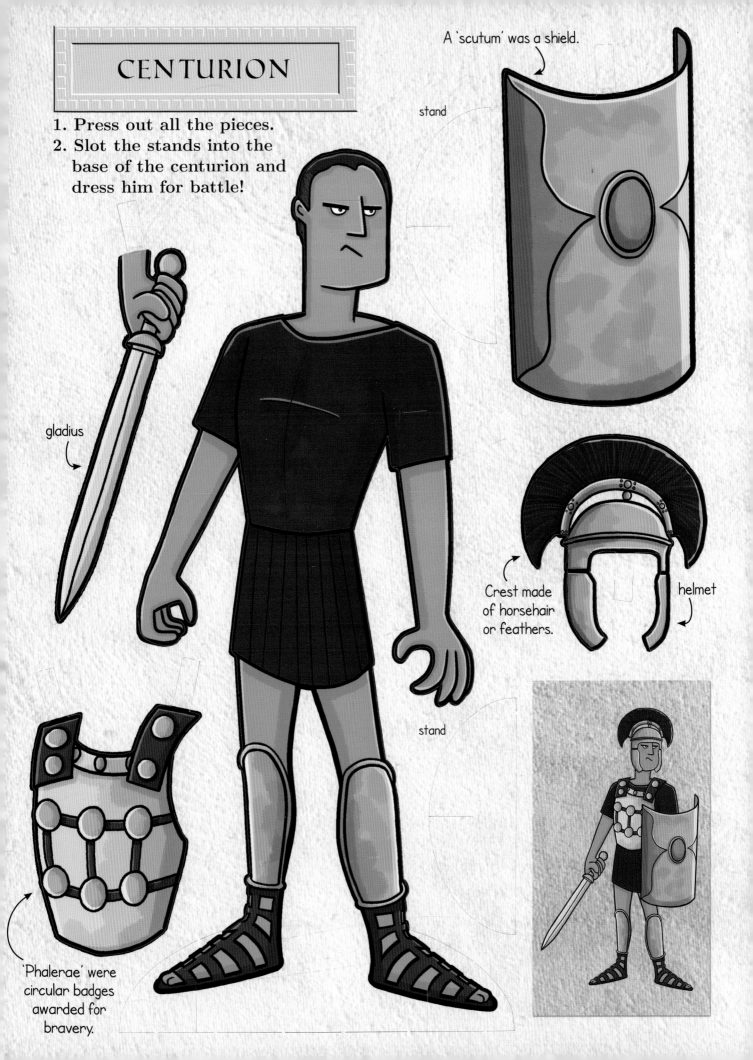

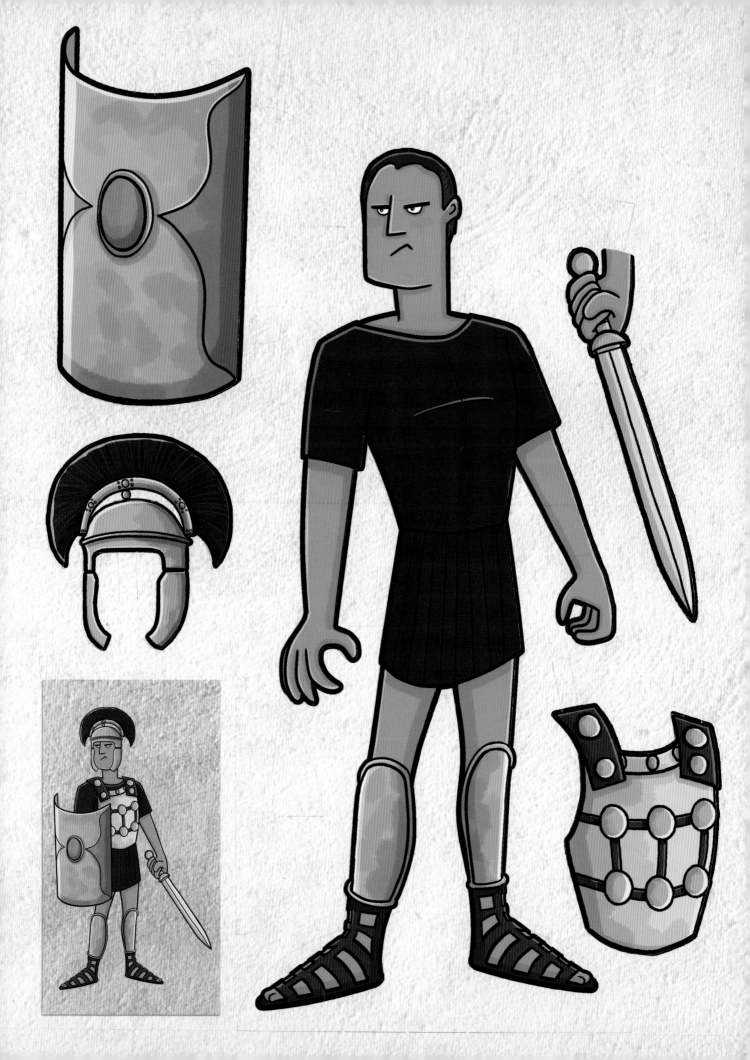

HAIL, EMPEROR!

1. Press out all the pieces.
2. Slot the stands into the base of the emperor and dress him for the games!

toga

stand

stand

Emperors decided who lived or died at gladiator games...

...if he stuck his thumb out it meant death to the loser!

A purple toga was called a 'trabea'. Only emperors could wear them.

Laurel wreaths were worn as crowns and were symbols of victory.

lions

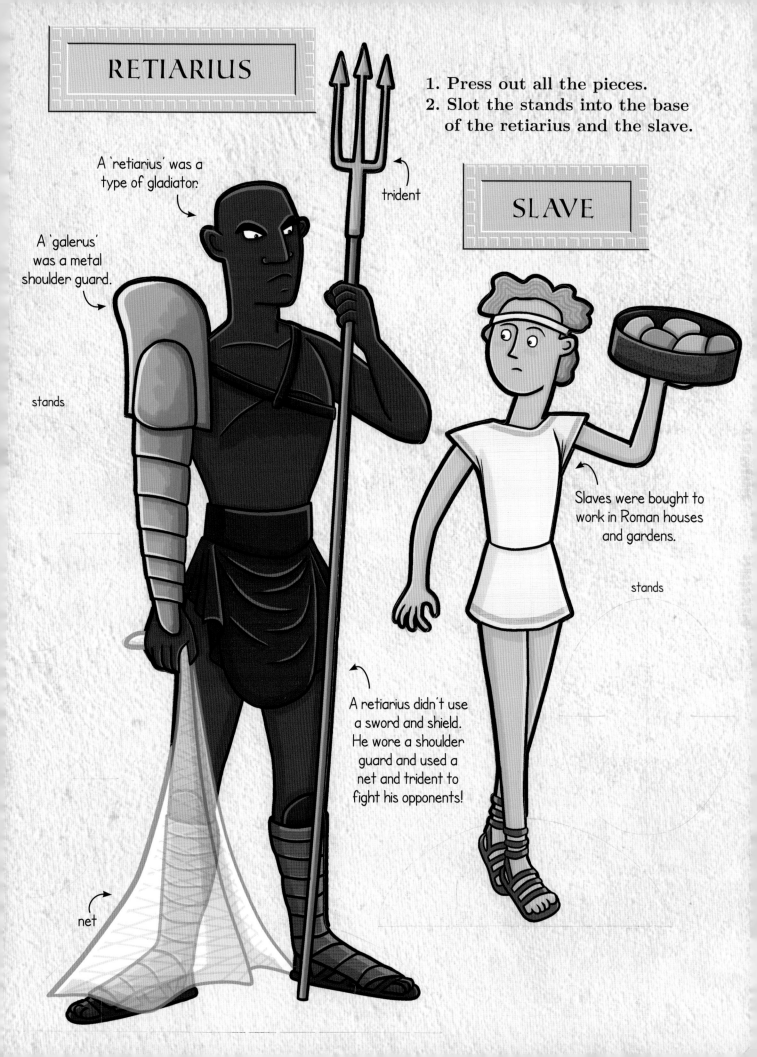

ROMAN JOBS

1. Press out all the pieces.
2. Slot a stand into the base of each character.

farmer

dentist

senator

hairdresser

Only Roman citizens were allowed to wear togas.

stands

stands

FEAST

1. Press out all
the pieces.

bed stands

wealthy Roman

slave

2. Slot stands into the base
of each item.

amphora

pigs'
ears

grapes

slave
stand

nettles

snails

table stands

1. Press out all the pieces.

Jupiter

stand

2. Slot a stand into the base of each god.

Mars

Apollo

stand

Venus

stand

Neptune

stands

GODS

CHARIOT RACING

1. Press out all the pieces.
2. Slot the stands into the base of the horse and chariot.

stands

Chariot races took place in a large, oval stadium called a 'circus'.

horse

Most chariots were pulled by one or two horses...

...but Emperor Nero's chariot was pulled by ten!

chariot

LIFE, LIVING AND LUNCH!

Romans loved art, music, poetry and plays. Wealthy Romans paid poets to write poems, musicians to sing songs and artists to create mosaics.

Mosaics were made out of hundreds of small, square pieces of painted pottery, stuck together to create a picture on the wall or a floor.

I'VE BEEN HOLDING STILL FOR WEEKS!

CAN YOU COMPLETE THIS MOSAIC?

COPY EACH SQUARE AND COLOUR!

HOLD STILL!

SCULPTURES

Wealthy Romans loved sculptures. They paid sculptors to carve statues out of a white stone called marble.

ROMAN FOOD

Ancient Romans bought their food at marketplaces called 'forums'. Spices were imported from distant lands, and the Romans ate weird and wonderful foods.

FOUL FACT!

ROMANS ATE GARUM WITH EVERYTHING. GARUM WAS A KIND OF KETCHUP MADE FROM ROTTEN FISH. THE ROMANS LOVED IT BUT IT SMELT SO BAD NO ONE WAS ALLOWED TO MAKE IT INSIDE THE CITY WALLS. YUCK!

FOOD FUN!

Follow the lines to see what's for dinner!

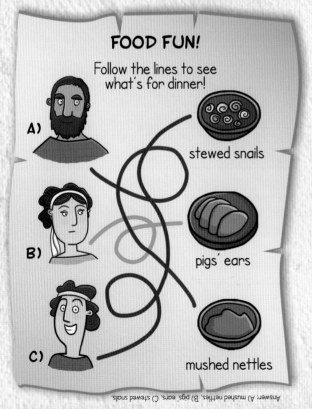

A)

stewed snails

B)

pigs' ears

C)

mushed nettles

COME DINE WITH A ROMAN!

At fancy Roman dinner parties you ate lying down.
If you needed the loo you had to...?

A)   ...STAY SEATED

B)   ...GO OUTSIDE

C)   ...LEAVE
      EARLY

Answer: A) mushed nettles, B) pigs' ears, C) stewed snails.

Answer: A) Stay seated! It was considered rude to leave the table for any reason.

SOLDIERS, SLAVES AND SENATORS

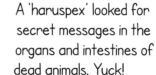

IF YOU WEREN'T A WEALTHY ROMAN THEN YOU HAD TO WORK. ROMANS HAD JOBS AS FARMERS, TEACHERS, LAWYERS AND BUILDERS, BUT SOME JOBS WERE A LITTLE UNUSUAL. DISCOVER THESE STRANGE JOBS BY MATCHING EACH PICTURE TO ITS CORRECT DESCRIPTION.

1. A 'haruspex' looked for secret messages in the organs and intestines of dead animals. Yuck!

2. A Roman dentist made false teeth from bones or wood, and had to know how to pull rotten teeth out with pliers and hot pokers!

3. A slave wasn't a job. It was a way of life. Slaves were bought and sold, and had to do whatever their owners told them to do.

4. An 'ornatrix' was a Roman hairdresser who had to know how to make brown hair dye out of rotten leeches and squid ink, and blonde hair dye out of pigeon poo, ashes and urine. Yuck!

5. A 'centurion' was a Roman soldier. All soldiers were Roman citizens and had to be over 25 years old. Soldiers could travel the world but had to stay in the army for at least 25 years!

Answer: 1-D, 2-C, 3-E, 4-B, 5-A.

A

B

C

D

E

1ˢᵗ Roman soldier: What's the time?
2ᴺᴰ ROMAN SOLDIER: XX PAST VII!

GOVERNMENT

Not all decisions were made by the emperor. The Romans had a government called the 'Senate'.

'SENATE' IS A LATIN WORD WHICH MEANS 'ASSEMBLY OF THE ELDERS'. THE SENATE ADVISED THE EMPEROR, DEBATED IMPORTANT ISSUES AND TRIED TO STOP ARMY GENERALS FROM STARTING BATTLES!

SHOW ME THE MONEY!

To be a senator, you had to be elected or nominated by the emperor. Only wealthy, noble Roman men could apply but before an election they had to…?

A) COOK ALL 600 SENATORS LUNCH

B) TAKE ALL THE SENATORS ON HOLIDAY

C) SHOW THE SENATE HOW RICH THEY WERE

Answer: c) They had to prove they had over one million sesterces (the Roman currency) invested in property. Nobles weren't allowed by law to earn money by working – they had to be wealthy by birth.

GRUESOME GAMES!

An emperor liked to keep his people happy, which meant plenty of entertainment in Ancient Rome. These gruesome games featured lots of blood and were a firm favourite with Roman audiences!

The games were usually deadly battles. The most popular events were the gladiator fights. Gladiators were skilled warriors who fought each other, wild animals or even slaves, all to the delight of the roaring Roman crowds.

ROMANS WATCHED THESE FEROCIOUS FIGHTS IN ENORMOUS, ROUND STADIUMS CALLED 'AMPHITHEATRES'. THESE HUGE STONE BUILDINGS COULD SEAT THOUSANDS OF PEOPLE. THE MOST FAMOUS AMPHITHEATRE OF THEM ALL IS THE COLOSSEUM IN ROME.

HOW MANY PEOPLE COULD SIT IN THE COLOSSEUM IN ROME?

A)   500 PEOPLE
B)   5000 PEOPLE
C)   50,000 PEOPLE

Answer: C) 50,000 people.

GLADIATORS WERE OFTEN SLAVES, CRIMINALS OR PRISONERS OF WAR BUT SOME MEN CHOSE TO FIGHT. IF YOU KEPT WINNING, YOU COULD EARN YOUR FREEDOM AND BE FAMOUS THROUGHOUT THE EMPIRE!

THE FIRST GLADIATORS FOUGHT AT FUNERALS INSTEAD OF GAMES. ROMANS BELIEVED THESE DEADLY FUNERAL FIGHTS HONOURED THEIR DEAD. WEIRD!

FOUL FACT!

What's a forum?
TWO-UM PLUS TWO-UM!

GODS AND GODDESSES

As soon as the Romans turned up and conquered your land, you had to lead a more Roman way of life. The Romans brought their language, architecture, currency, art and lifestyle to all their settlements.

The Romans also brought their religious beliefs to their new lands. The Romans worshipped gods for nearly everything, for example: a god for telling the truth, a god of good luck, goddesses of toothache and flowers, and even a god of doors!

WHICH IS WHICH?

Follow the lines to discover what each god was worshipped for.

VENUS

JUPITER

MARS

NEPTUNE

IT WAS VERY CONFUSING! OUR OLD GODS WERE OUT AND SUDDENLY THERE WERE ALL THESE NEW, FANCY ROMAN GODS TO WORSHIP!

WAR   WATER   BEAUTY   THUNDER

Answer: Venus = beauty, Jupiter = thunder, Mars = war, Neptune = water

What did Caesar say when he got home? ROME, SWEET ROME!

SUPER GODS SWAP!

In a conquered land, the Romans often combined native gods with their Roman gods, creating new, super gods for everyone to worship. Many British gods and goddesses had Roman makeovers!

HI! I'M SULIS MINERVA. I WAS JUST PLAIN OLD SULIS, CELTIC GODDESS OF THE HOT SPRINGS IN BATH, ENGLAND. BUT WHEN THE ROMANS ARRIVED I BECAME A BRAND NEW ROMANO-BRITISH GODDESS! I WAS WORSHIPPED FOR HEALTH, LIFE AND WISDOM. OH, I ALSO CURSE PEOPLE TOO, SO DON'T UPSET ME... ...OK?

MULTI-TALENTED!

Apollo wins the prize for 'God Who Was Worshipped For Lots of Things'! Draw a circle around each of the words below that you think Apollo was worshipped for.

ART   MUSIC   SUN

LIGHT

MEDICINE   HEALING

POETRY   TRUTH

PROPHECY

SICKNESS

ARCHERY

PLAGUE   FARMING

Answer: Apollo was god of all of them!